PHOTOCOPIABLE
Mental Arithmetic Questions for Year 2

Helen Maden

Published by

TOPICAL RESOURCES

by Helen Maden

Mental Arithmetic Questions for Year 2 is the first of a series of five books which provide a bank of easily accessible Mental Arithmetic Questions for use in a variety of classroom situations. It contains thirty different exercises which progressively get harder. Each exercise includes: Teacher Questions suitable for reading aloud, all answers needed and a photocopiable Pupil Answer Sheet with prompts given where necessary.

This book includes work from: The National Curriculum Levels 1 and 2, mathematical problems using numbers up to 200 and concepts taken from The National Numeracy Strategy Key Objectives for Year Two.

Topical Resources publishes a range of Educational Materials for use in Primary Schools and Pre-School Nurseries and Playgroups.

For latest catalogue:
Tel: 01772 863158
Fax: 01772 866153

E.Mail: sales@topical-resources.co.uk
Visit our Website on:
www.topical-resources.co.uk

Printed in Great Britain for "Topical Resources", Publishers of Educational Materials, P.O. Box 329, Broughton, Preston, PR3 5LT by T.Snape & Company Ltd, Boltons Court, Preston, England.

Typeset by Paul Sealey Illustration and Design, 3 Wentworth Drive, Thornton, England. FY5 5AR.

First Published May 2003.
ISBN 1 872977 76 6

Contents

Teacher's Notes

How the Books are Organised

This book is one of a series of five. It contains thirty Mental Arithmetic exercises which use a wide mathematical vocabulary as advocated in The National Numeracy Strategy. Each exercise consists of a page of Teacher Questions together with answers and a photocopiable Pupil Answer Sheet complete with all necessary prompts. The book also includes a master for a Teacher's Record Sheet.

Each exercise is laid out in a similar way. Repetitive questions allow the children to become familiar with a large variety of problems. To make the activities suitably taxing, the questions progress from easy at the beginning of the book to harder ones towards the end.

The **Year 2** book includes work from The National Curriculum Levels 1 and 2, mathematical problems using numbers up to 200 and concepts taken from The National Numeracy Strategy Key Objectives for Year Two.

Book 1 which is aimed at **Year 3** includes work from The National Curriculum Levels 2 and 3, mathematical problems using numbers up to 500 and concepts taken from The National Numeracy Strategy Key Objectives for Year Three.

Book 2 which is aimed at **Year 4** includes work from The National Curriculum Levels 2, 3 and 4, mathematical problems using numbers up to 1,000 and concepts taken from The National Numeracy Strategy Key Objectives for Year Four.

Book 3 which is aimed at **Year 5** includes work from The National Curriculum Levels 3 and 4, mathematical problems using numbers up to 10,000 and concepts taken from The National Numeracy Strategy Key Objectives for Year Five.

Book 4 which is aimed at **Year 6** includes work from The National Curriculum Levels 3, 4 and 5, mathematical problems using numbers up to 1,000,000 and concepts taken from The National Numeracy Strategy Key Objectives for Year Six.

How to Use the Questions

The questions in this book could be used in a number of different ways including:

(1) As the basis of quick fire mental oral work to be used at the introduction of a mathematics lesson.

(2) As a Diagnostic Test to assess understanding and ability to solve Mental Arithmetic questions.

(3) As preparation for end of year SAT tests.

The exercises in this book may be used to suggest questions for use in the quick fire oral mental session found at the beginning of every numeracy lesson. One approach could be to teach and practice questions of a similar type to those found on the exercise chosen for that week and then use the exercise as an assessment at the end of the week.

Using the exercises as a diagnostic aid would involve carrying out a test with the children, then to mark the work, identify common misconceptions and use this information to inform planning and subsequent teaching. The children could then be re-tested at a later date to assess improvements made.

If the exercises were to be used to prepare children for annual SAT tests, the teacher would read each question twice, leaving a short gap in-between. There is no time limit on each question, so the length of time taken will depend on the speed of the children. Proceed from one question to the next when you feel that all the children have had ample opportunity to find the answer.

Children are allowed to use space on the test paper for working out their answers if necessary.

The Teacher's Record Sheet

A teacher's record sheet is provided (page 64) in order to keep track of the progress of each individual child. Spaces are provided to record the score obtained on each test. (N.B. Most tests are marked out of 8. However, the tests containing the grids only have space for 7 questions. These are shown in the shaded columns.) This record can be used to identify pupils who need extra support, or those that need more challenging material which can be found in the subsequent books in the series.

Mental Arithmetic Test 1   Questions to be Read to the Children

Ask the children to look at their printed answer sheet.
Explain:
- *the boxes are for you to write your answers in;*
- *the letters below each box show you which box to use for each question;*
- *you can do any working out in the white spaces around the boxes, if you need to.*

Where necessary, you can show the children how to draw a tick, cross etc.
Remember to repeat each question.

Question 1
Look at the grid.
I want you to find some numbers on the grid.
Put a ring around these numbers.
31 – 14 – 43   *Answer =* (31) (14) (43)

Question 2
Find box a.
Look at the numbers inside box a.
Circle the number that is nearest to 5.   *Answer =* (7)

Question 3
Find box b.
What is 2 less than 5?
Write your answer inside box b.   *Answer = 3*

Question 4
Find box c.
Look at the numbers inside box c.
Circle the number that is the nearest 10 to 61   *Answer =* (60)

Question 5
Look carefully at the shapes.
Tick the shape with exactly 2 straight sides.

Answer =

Question 6
Look at the pieces of fruit.
Jake spent 10p altogether.
He bought a lemon for 9p.
Tick the other fruit he bought.   *Answer = cherry*

Question 7
Find box d.
What is the difference between 19 and 12?
Write your answer in box d.   *Answer = 7*

Name: _____

Question 1

0	1	2	3	4	5	6	7	8	9
10	11	12	13	14	15	16	17	18	19
20	21	22	23	24	25	26	27	28	29
30	31	32	33	34	35	36	37	38	39
40	41	42	43	44	45	46	47	48	49

Question 2

7	12
10	
20	16

a

Question 3

b

Question 4

60	40
50	
80	70

c

Question 5

Question 6

grape 2p

banana 10p

apple 5p

cherry 1p

Question 7

d

Ask the children to look at their printed answer sheet.
Explain:
- *the boxes are for you to write your answers in;*
- *the letters below each box show you which box to use for each question;*
- *you can do any working out in the white spaces around the boxes, if you need to.*

Where necessary, you can show the children how to draw a tick, cross etc.
Remember to repeat each question.

Question 1
Find box a.
Fiona is 3 years old. Stewart is 6 years old.
How much older is Stewart than Fiona?
Write your answer in box a.   Answer = 3 years

Question 2
Find box b.
What is 2 more than 8?
Write your answer in box b.   Answer = 10

Question 3
Find box c.
What is 20 add 4?
Write your answer inside box c.   Answer = 24

Question 4
Find box d.
What is the next number in this sequence?
3 – 6 – 9
Write your answer in box d.   Answer = 12

Question 5
Find box e.
There are 10 sweets in a packet.
How many packets do you need so that 24 children can have 1 sweet each?
Write your answer in box e.   Answer = 3 packets

Question 6
Find box f.
How many tens in 54?
Write your answer in box f.   Answer = 5 tens

Question 7
Find box g.
What number is shown by the arrow?
Write your answer in box g.   Answer = 3

Question 8
Look carefully at the shapes.
Tick the pentagon.   Answer =

Name: _____

Question 1

years

a

Question 2

b

Question 3

c

Question 4

d

Question 5

packets

e

Question 6

tens

f

Question 7

0   ↓   5   10

g

Question 8

Mental Arithmetic Test 3   Questions to be Read to the Children

Ask the children to look at their printed answer sheet.
Explain:
- *the boxes are for you to write your answers in;*
- *the letters below each box show you which box to use for each question;*
- *you can do any working out in the white spaces around the boxes, if you need to.*

Where necessary, you can show the children how to draw a tick, cross etc.
Remember to repeat each question.

Question 1
Find box a.
Write one hundred and one as a number.
Write your answer in box a.   Answer = 101

Question 2
Find box b.
What is the number after 39?
Write your answer in box b.   Answer = 40

Question 3
Find box c.
Think of one odd number that is more than 5 and less than 20.   (One of these:)
Write your number inside box c.   Answer = 7, 9, 11,13,15,17,19

Question 4
Find box d.
Owen has 5 candles on his cake. He blows out 3.
How many candles are left alight?
Write your answer in box d.   Answer = 2 candles

Question 5
Find box e.
What is 7 add 8?
Write your answer in box e.   Answer = 15

Question 6
Look at the coins.
Peter wants to buy an apple for 15p.
Tick the coins he should use to give the corect amount.   Answer = 10p & 5p

---

Question 7
Find box f.
What is half of 10?
Write your answer in box f.   Answer = 5

Question 8
Look carefully at the shapes.
Tick the shape that is not a hexagon.   Answer =

Name: _____

Question 1

a

Question 2

b

Question 3

c

Question 4

candles

d

Question 5

e

Question 6

(10p)   (2p)   (5p)   (1p)

Question 7

f

Question 8

9

Ask the children to look at their printed answer sheet.
Explain:
- *the boxes are for you to write your answers in;*
- *the letters below each box show you which box to use for each question;*
- *you can do any working out in the white spaces around the boxes, if you need to.*

Where necessary, you can show the children how to draw a tick, cross etc.
Remember to repeat each question.

Question 1
Find box a.
Heather has 9p. Fiona has 6p.
How much money do they have together?
Write your answer in box a.

Answer = 15p

Question 2
Look at the graph.
It shows children's favourite colours.
How many more children like green than red?
Write your answer in box b.

Answer = 2 children

Question 3
Find box c.
What is the difference between 19 and 15?
Write your answer in box c.

Answer = 4

Question 4
Find box d.
Look carefully at the numbers in the box.
Circle the number that is nearest to 10.

Answer = ⑪

Question 5
Find the clock face.
Jan wakes up at 6 o'clock.
She gets up 1 hour later.
Draw, on the clock, the time she gets up.

Answer =

Question 6
Find box e.
What is 3 less than 6?
Write your answer in box e.

Answer = 3

Question 7
Find box f.
Circle the number that is the nearest 10 to 19.

Answer = ⑳

Question 8
Look carefully at the shapes.
Tick the shape that does not have a right angle.

Answer =

Name: _____

Question 1

pence

a

Question 5

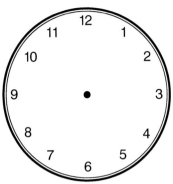

Question 2

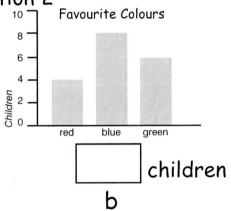

Favourite Colours

children

b

Question 6

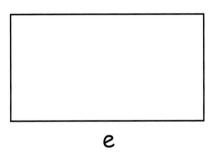

e

Question 3

c

Question 7

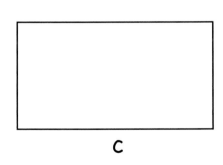

20		90
	10	
50		40

f

Question 4

11		20
	14	
16		19

d

Question 8

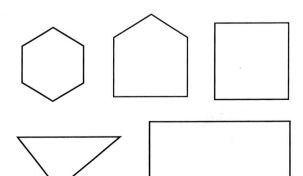

Ask the children to look at their printed answer sheet.
Explain:
* *the boxes are for you to write your answers in;*
* *the letters below each box show you which box to use for each question;*
* *you can do any working out in the white spaces around the boxes, if you need to.*

Where necessary, you can show the children how to draw a tick, cross etc.
Remember to repeat each question.

Question 1
Look at the grid.
I want you to find some numbers on the grid.
Put a ring round these numbers.
48 – 24 – 12

Answer = ⑭⑧ ㉔ ⑫

Question 2
Find box a.
Write one hundred and ninety nine as a number.
Write your answer in box a.

Answer = 199

Question 3
Find box b.
What is 3 more than 6?
Write your answer in box b.

Answer = 9

Question 4
Find box c.
How many tens are in 69?
Write your answer in box c.

Answer = 6 tens

Question 5
Look carefully at the shapes.
Tick the hexagon.

Answer =

Question 6
Find box d.
Anna has a bunch of 5 grapes.
She eats 2 grapes. How many does she have left?
Write your answer in box d.

Answer = 3 grapes

Question 7
Find box e.
What is 30 add 9?
Write your answer in box e.

Answer = 39

Name: _____

Question 1

0	1	2	3	4	5	6	7	8	9
10	11	12	13	14	15	16	17	18	19
20	21	22	23	24	25	26	27	28	29
30	31	32	33	34	35	36	37	38	39
40	41	42	43	44	45	46	47	48	49

Question 2

a

Question 5

Question 3

b

Question 6

grapes

d

Question 4

tens

c

Question 7

e

13

Ask the children to look at their printed answer sheet.
Explain:
- *the boxes are for you to write your answers in;*
- *the letters below each box show you which box to use for each question;*
- *you can do any working out in the white spaces around the boxes, if you need to.*

Where necessary, you can show the children how to draw a tick, cross etc.
Remember to repeat each question.

Question 1
Find box a.
There are 10 lollies in a box.
How many boxes do you need so that 31 children can have a lolly each?
Write your answer in box a.   *Answer = 4 boxes*

Question 2
Find box b.
What is the next number in this sequence?
10 – 20 – 30
Write your answer in box b.   *Answer = 40*

Question 3
Look at the drawing above box c.
What number is shown by the arrow?
Write your answer in box c.   *Answer = 7*

Question 4
Find box d.
What is half of 20?
Write your answer in box d.   *Answer = 10*

Question 5
Look at the fruit.
Conner spent 10p on fruit.
He bought a pear and another fruit.
Tick the fruit that Conner bought.   *Answer = pear & apple*

Question 6
Find box e.
Think of one even number that is more than 5 but less than 20.   *(One of these:)*
Write your number in box e.   *Answer = 6, 8,10,12,14,16,18*

Question 7
Find box f.
What is the difference between 17 and 14?
Write your answer in box f.   *Answer = 3*

Question 8
Look at the shapes.
Tick the shape that has 6 sides.   *Answer =*

Name: _____

Question 1

boxes

a

Question 5

pear 5p

apple 5p

banana 10p

lemon 20p

melon 50p

Question 2

b

Question 6

e

Question 3

0   5   ↓   10

c

Question 7

f

Question 4

d

Question 8

15

Ask the children to look at their printed answer sheet.

Explain:

- *the boxes are for you to write your answers in;*
- *the letters below each box show you which box to use for each question;*
- *you can do any working out in the white spaces around the boxes, if you need to.*

Where necessary, you can show the children how to draw a tick, cross etc.
Remember to repeat each question.

Question 1
Find box a.
What is 4 less than 7?
Write your answer in box a.   Answer = 3

Question 2
Look at the coins.
Alison wants to buy a packet of sweets.
The sweets cost 12p.
Tick the coins Alison will need to use to give the correct amount.   Answer = 10p & 2p

---

Question 3
Find box b.
Look carefully at the numbers in the box.
Circle the number that is nearest to 6.   Answer = ⑧

Question 4
Find box c.
What is 20 add 6?
Write your answer in box c.   Answer = 26

Question 5
Look at the cross in the circle.
If you move the cross through a quarter turn, what position would it be in?
Tick one box for your answer.   Answer = ⊞

Question 6
Find box d.
Gerry is 2 years old. Mary is 9 years old.
How much older is Mary than Gerry?
Write your answer in box d.   Answer = 7 years

Question 7
Find box e.
There are 10 children in a group. Half are boys and half are girls.
How many girls are there?
Write your answer in box e.   Answer = 5 girls

Question 8
Look at the shapes.
Tick the shape with only 1 straight side.   Answer =

Name: _____

Question 1

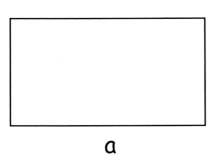

a

Question 2

10p   5p   2p   1p

Question 3

8		10
	12	
16		15

b

Question 4

c

Question 5

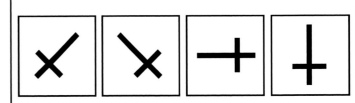

Question 6

years

d

Question 7

girls

e

Question 8

Mental Arithmetic Test 8   Questions to be Read to the Children

Ask the children to look at their printed answer sheet.
Explain:
* *the boxes are for you to write your answers in;*
* *the letters below each box show you which box to use for each question;*
* *you can do any working out in the white spaces around the boxes, if you need to.*

Where necessary, you can show the children how to draw a tick, cross etc.
Remember to repeat each question.

Question 1
Find the clock face.
Sue has her tea at 5 o'clock.
She goes out 2 hours later. What time does she go out?
Draw, on the clock, the time Sue goes out.   Answer =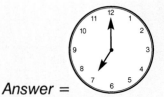

Question 2
Find box a.
Carolyn has 10p. Chloe has 5p.
How much money do they have altogether?
Write your answer in box a.   Answer = 15p

Question 3
Find box b.
Joshua has 10 candles on his cake. He blows out 8 candles.
How many candles were left alight?
Write your answer in box b.   Answer = 2 candles

Question 4
Look at the drawing above box c.
What number is shown by the arrow?
Write your answer in box c.   Answer = 1

Question 5
Find box d.
What is 10 add 4?
Write your answer in box d.   Answer = 14

Question 6
Find box e.
How many tens are there in 88?
Write your answer in box e.   Answer = 8 tens

Question 7
Find box f.
Circle the number that is the nearest 10 to 64.   Answer =

Question 8
Look carefully at the shapes.
Tick the shape that is not a pentagon.   Answer =

Mental
Arithmetic
Test 8

Name: _____

Pupil Answer
Sheet

Question 1

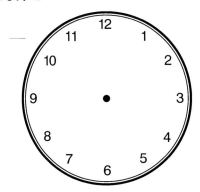

Question 5

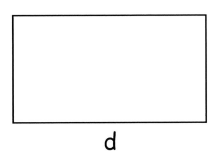

d

Question 2

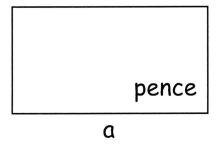

pence

a

Question 6

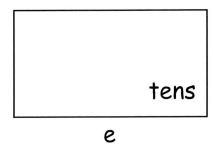

tens

e

Question 3

candles

b

Question 7

60		80
	70	
40		90

f

Question 4

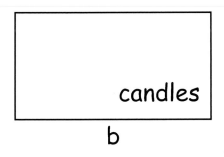

c

Question 8

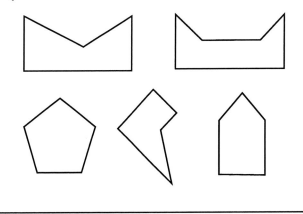

Ask the children to look at their printed answer sheet.
Explain:
- *the boxes are for you to write your answers in;*
- *the letters below each box show you which box to use for each question;*
- *you can do any working out in the white spaces around the boxes, if you need to.*

Where necessary, you can show the children how to draw a tick, cross etc.
Remember to repeat each question.

Question 1
Find box a.
What is the difference between 14 and 12?
Write your answer in box a.   Answer = 2

Question 2
Find box b.
What is 50 add 4?
Write your answer in box b.   Answer = 54

Question 3
Find box c.
Think of one even number that is more than 25 and less than 40.   (One of these:)
Write your number in box c.   Answer = 26, 28, 30, 32,
34, 36, 38

Question 4
Find box d.
Write one hundred and seven as a number.
Write your answer in box d.   Answer = 107

Question 5
Find box e.
What is 2 more than 10?
Write your answer in box e.   Answer = 12

Question 6
Find box f.
What is half of 4?
Write your answer in box f.   Answer = 2

Question 7
Find box g.
Jessica is 8 years old. Michael is 11 years old.
How much older is Michael than Jessica?
Write your answer in box g.   Answer = 3 years

Question 8
Look at the 3D shapes. Tick the cuboid.   Answer =

Mental
Arithmetic
Test 9

Name: _____

Pupil Answer
Sheet

Question 1

a

Question 5

e

Question 2

b

Question 6

f

Question 3

c

Question 7

years

g

Question 4

d

Question 8

Mental Arithmetic Test 10   Questions to be Read to the Children

Ask the children to look at their printed answer sheet.
Explain:
- *the boxes are for you to write your answers in;*
- *the letters below each box show you which box to use for each question;*
- *you can do any working out in the white spaces around the boxes, if you need to.*

Where necessary, you can show the children how to draw a tick, cross etc.
Remember to repeat each question.

- -

Question 1
Look at the grid.
I want you to find some numbers on the grid.
Put a ring around these numbers.
34 – 42 – 18   Answer =

- -

Question 2
Look at the clock face.
Christine gets up at half past 7.
She sets off for school 1 hour later.
What time does Christine set off for school?
Draw, on the clock, the time Christine sets off.   Answer =

- -

Question 3
Find box a.
What is the next number in this sequence?
2 – 4 – 6 – 8 – 10
Write your answer in box a.   Answer = 12

- -

Question 4
Look at the graph above box b.
This graph shows how children get to school.
How many more children walk than go by car?
Write your answer in box b.   Answer = 4 children

- -

Question 5
Look carefully at the shapes.
Tick the shape that does not have a right angle.   Answer =

- -

Question 6
Find box c.
There are 10 sweets in one packet.
How many packets do you need so that 26 children can
have one sweet each?
Write your answer in box c.   Answer = 3 packets

- -

Question 7
Find box d.
Look carefully at the numbers in the box.
Circle the number that is nearest to 10.   Answer = 12

- -

Mental
Arithmetic
Test 10

Name: _____

Question 1

0	1	2	3	4	5	6	7	8	9
10	11	12	13	14	15	16	17	18	19
20	21	22	23	24	25	26	27	28	29
30	31	32	33	34	35	36	37	38	39
40	41	42	43	44	45	46	47	48	49

Question 2

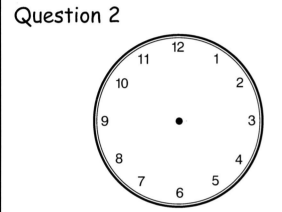

Question 5

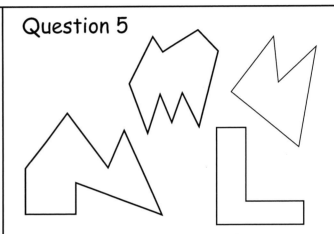

Question 3

a

Question 6

packets

c

Question 4

Ways to get to school

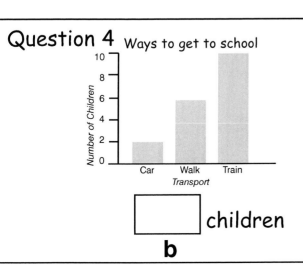

children

b

Question 7

12		17
	15	
18		19

d

Mental Arithmetic Test 11   Questions to be Read to the Children

Ask the children to look at their printed answer sheet.
Explain:
- *the boxes are for you to write your answers in;*
- *the letters below each box show you which box to use for each question;*
- *you can do any working out in the white spaces around the boxes, if you need to.*

Where necessary, you can show the children how to draw a tick, cross etc.
Remember to repeat each question.

Question 1
Find box a.
How many tens are there in 43?
Write your answer in box a.   Answer = 4 tens

Question 2
Find box b.
Hannah has a bunch of 10 grapes.
She eats 4 grapes. How many are left?
Write your answer in box b.   Answer = 6 grapes

Question 3
Find box c.
What is half of 22?
Write your answer in box c.   Answer = 11

Question 4
Find box d.
Mrs Sheridan has 6 packets of crayons.
There are 10 crayons in each packet.
How many crayons does she have altogether?
Write your answer in box d.   Answer = 60 crayons

Question 5
Look at the snowman in the circle.
If you turned it through half a turn, what position would it be in?
Tick one box for your answer   Answer =

Question 6
Look at the coins.
Oliver wants to buy an apple that costs 7p.
Tick the coins he should use to give the correct amount.   Answer = 5p & 2p

----

Question 7
Find box e.
What is 3 less than 8?
Write your answer in box e.   Answer = 5

Question 8
Look carefully at the shapes.
Tick the shape that is not a square.   Answer =

Question 1

tens

a

Question 2

grapes

b

Question 3

c

Question 4

crayons

d

Question 5

Question 6

10p   5p   2p   1p

Question 7

e

Question 8

25

Mental Arithmetic Test 12   Questions to be Read to the Children

Ask the children to look at their printed answer sheet.
Explain:
* the boxes are for you to write your answers in;
* the letters below each box show you which box to use for each question;
* you can do any working out in the white spaces around the boxes, if you need to.

Where necessary, you can show the children how to draw a tick, cross etc.
Remember to repeat each question.

Question 1
Find box a.
There are 12 children in a group.
Half are boys and half are girls. How many are girls?
Write your answer in box a.

Answer = 6 girls

Question 2
Find box b.
Listen to these numbers.
42 – 43 – 44 – 46 – 47
Write in box b the number I have missed out.

Answer = 45

Question 3
Bethany buys an apple for 10p and another fruit.
She pays 20p altogether.
Tick the other fruit she buys.

Answer = pear

Question 4
Find box c.
What is the difference between 15 and 17?
Write your answer in box c.

Answer = 2

Question 5
Find box d.
Write one hundred and seventy two as a number.
Write your answer in box d.

Answer = 172

Question 6
Find box e.
Think of an even number that is more than 40 but less than 50.
Write your answer in box e.

(One of these:)
Answer = 42, 44, 46, 48

Question 7
Look at the drawing above box f.
What number is shown by the arrow?
Write your answer in box f.

Answer = 5

Question 8
Look at the shapes.
Tick the shape with only one straight side.

Answer =

Name: _____

Question 1

girls

a

Question 2

b

Question 3

apple 10p

pear 10p

banana 15p

lemon 20p

Question 4

c

Question 5

d

Question 6

e

Question 7

0   ↓   10

f

Question 8

Mental Arithmetic Test 13   Questions to be Read to the Children

Ask the children to look at their printed answer sheet.
Explain:
* the boxes are for you to write your answers in;
* the letters below each box show you which box to use for each question;
* you can do any working out in the white spaces around the boxes, if you need to.

Where necessary, you can show the children how to draw a tick, cross etc.
Remember to repeat each question.

Question 1
Amit had his tea at 6 o'clock.
He went to bed two hours later.
At what time did Amit go to bed?
Draw, on the clock, the time he went to bed.

Answer =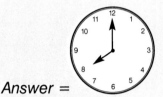

Question 2
Find box a.
There are ten lollies in one box.
How many boxes of lollies do you need so that 29 children can
have one lolly each?
Write your answer in box a.

Answer = 3 boxes

Question 3
Find box b.
What is 2 more than 14?
Write your answer in box b.

Answer = 16

Question 4
Look carefully at the numbers in box c.
Circle the number which is nearest to ten.

Answer = ⑨

Question 5
Find box d.
What is 40 add 6?
Write your answer in box d.

Answer = 46

Question 6
Find box e.
What is the next number in this sequence?
1 – 3 – 5 – 7
Write your answer in box e.

Answer = 9

Question 7
Find box f. Sam is 8 years old.
His sister Holly is 5 years old.
How much older is Sam than Holly?
Write your answer in box f.

Answer = 3 years

Question 8
Look at these shapes.
Tick the shape with 5 sides.

Answer =

Name: _____

Question 1

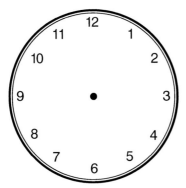

Question 5

d

Question 2

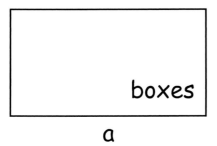

boxes

a

Question 6

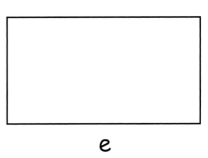

e

Question 3

b

Question 7

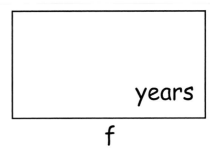

years

f

Question 4

9	20
15	
7	5

c

Question

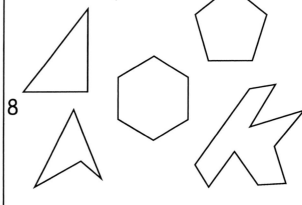

8

Ask the children to look at their printed answer sheet.
Explain:
* *the boxes are for you to write your answers in;*
* *the letters below each box show you which box to use for each question;*
* *you can do any working out in the white spaces around the boxes, if you need to.*

Where necessary, you can show the children how to draw a tick, cross etc.
Remember to repeat each question.

Question 1
Look at the grid.
I want you to find some numbers on the grid.
Put a ring round these numbers.
41 – 16 – 25.

Answer = (41) (16) (25)

Question 2
Find box a.
Thomas has ten peas on his plate.
He drops one on the floor. How many peas are left on the plate?
Write your answer in box a.

Answer = 9 peas

Question 3
Look at the coins.
Gabby wants to buy some sweets which cost 8p.
Tick the coins that she should use to give the correct amount.

Answer = 5p, 2p, 1p.

Question 4
Find box b.
What is 3 less than 12?
Write your answer in box b.

Answer = 9

Question 5
Look carefully at the shapes.
Put a tick on the shape that is not a rectangle.

Answer =

Question 6
Find box c.
How many tens are there in 79?
Write your answer in box c.

Answer = 7 tens

Question 7
Find box d.
Write one hundred and ninety as a number.
Write your answer in box d.

Answer = 190

Name: _____

Question 1

0	1	2	3	4	5	6	7	8	9
10	11	12	13	14	15	16	17	18	19
20	21	22	23	24	25	26	27	28	29
30	31	32	33	34	35	36	37	38	39
40	41	42	43	44	45	46	47	48	49

Question 2

peas

a

Question 5

Question 3

10p 5p 2p 1p

10p 1p

Question 6

tens

c

Question 4

b

Question 7

d

Ask the children to look at their printed answer sheet.
Explain:
- *the boxes are for you to write your answers in;*
- *the letters below each box show you which box to use for each question;*
- *you can do any working out in the white spaces around the boxes, if you need to.*

Where necessary, you can show the children how to draw a tick, cross etc.
Remember to repeat each question.

Question 1
Look at the graph above box a.
It shows children's favourite colours.
How many more children like yellow than red?
Write your answer in box a.   Answer = 6 children

Question 2
Find box b.
Think of one odd number that is more than 20 but less than 30.   (One of these:)
Write your answer in box b.   Answer = 21, 23, 25, 27, 29

Question 3
Find box c.
A clover has 3 leaves.
How many leaves will 4 clovers have?
Write your answer in box c.   Answer = 12 leaves

Question 4
Find box d.
What is half of 12?
Write your answer in box d.   Answer = 6

Question 5
Find box e.
Circle the number that is the nearest 10 to 76.   Answer = (80)

Question 6
Look at the clock face. Sarah got up at 8 o'clock.
She caught a bus two hours later.
Draw, on the clock, the time she got on the bus.   Answer =

Question 7
Find box f.
What is the difference between 17 and 11?
Write your answer in box f.   Answer = 6

Question 8
Look at the shapes.
Tick the shape with exactly two curved sides.   Answer =

Name: _____

Question 1

Favourite colours

[bar chart: Children (y-axis 0 to 10) vs Colours (red, yellow, blue)]

[ ] children
a

Question 2

[ ]
b

Question 3

[ ] leaves
c

Question 4

[ ]
d

Question 5

40		90
	60	
70		80

e

Question 6

[clock face]

Question 7

[ ]
f

Question 8

[shapes]

Ask the children to look at their printed answer sheet.
Explain:
- *the boxes are for you to write your answers in;*
- *the letters below each box show you which box to use for each question;*
- *you can do any working out in the white spaces around the boxes, if you need to.*

Where necessary, you can show the children how to draw a tick, cross etc.
Remember to repeat each question.

Question 1
Look at the arrow in the circle.
If you moved the arrow through half a turn, what position would it be in?
Tick one box for your answer.

Answer =

Question 2
Find box a.
What is 70 add 5?
Write your answer in box a.

Answer = 75

Question 3
Find box b.
Look at the five numbers in the box.
Circle the number that is nearest to 6.

Answer = 5

Question 4
Find box c.
There are 20 children in a class.
Half are boys and half are girls. How many children are boys?
Write your answer in box c.

Answer = 10 boys

Question 5
Find box d.
Hannah is 8 years old. Her brother Joshua is 10 years old.
How much older is Joshua than Hannah?
Write your answer in box d.

Answer = 2 years

Question 6
Find box e.
Listen to these numbers. 71 – 72 – 74 – 75
Write the number I have missed out in box e.

Answer = 73

Question 7
Rachel spends 20p altogether.
She buys a lemon for 15p and another fruit.
Tick the fruit she buys.

Answer = pear

Question 8
Look at the 3D shapes.
Tick the cube.

Answer =

Name: _____

Question 1

Question 2

a

Question 3

5		8
	4	
2		10

b

Question 4

boys

c

Question 5

years

d

Question 6

e

Question 7

pear 5p   apple 4p

kiwi 20p

melon 6p   lemon 15p

Question 8

Mental Arithmetic Test 17   Questions to be Read to the Children

Ask the children to look at their printed answer sheet.
Explain:
- *the boxes are for you to write your answers in;*
- *the letters below each box show you which box to use for each question;*
- *you can do any working out in the white spaces around the boxes, if you need to.*

Where necessary, you can show the children how to draw a tick, cross etc.
Remember to repeat each question.

Question 1
Find box a.
Write one hundred and nine as a number.
Write your answer in box a.   Answer = 109

Question 2
Find box b.
Daniel has 10 sweets. He eats 3 sweets.
How many does he have left?
Write your answer in box b.   Answer = 7 sweets

Question 3
Look at the clock face.
Vikki has her lunch at 12 o'clock on Saturdays.
She goes to ballet one and a half hours later.
Draw, on the clock face, the time Vikki goes to ballet.   Answer =

Question 4
Find box c.
Think of an even number that is more than 10 but less than 20.   (one of these:)
Write your answer in box c.   Answer = 12, 14, 16, 18

Question 5
Find box d.
Neil had 2 apples and Andrew had 11.
How many apples did they have altogether?
Write your answer in box d.   Answer = 13 apples

Question 6
Find box e.
What is 3 more than 15?
Write your answer in box e.   Answer = 18

Question 7
Find box f.
What is 2 less than 11?
Write your answer in box f.   Answer = 9

Question 8
Look carefully at the shapes.
Tick the shape that does not have a right angle.   Answer =

Name: _____

Question 1	Question 5
a	apples d
Question 2	Question 6
sweets b	e
Question 3	Question 7
(clock face showing numbers 1-12)	f
Question 4	Question 8
c	(shapes)

Ask the children to look at their printed answer sheet.
Explain:
* *the boxes are for you to write your answers in;*
* *the letters below each box show you which box to use for each question;*
* *you can do any working out in the white spaces around the boxes, if you need to.*

Where necessary, you can show the children how to draw a tick, cross etc.
Remember to repeat each question.

Question 1
Look at the grid. I want you to find some numbers on the grid.
Put a ring around these numbers.
35 – 13 – 27   Answer =   35 13 27

Question 2
Find box a.
There are 10 sweets in a packet.
How many packets do you need so
that 43 children can have 1 sweet each?
Write your answer in box a.   Answer = 5 packets

Question 3
Find box b.
How many tens are there in 16?
Write your answer in box b.   Answer = 1 ten

Question 4
Find box c.
What is half of 18?
Write your answer in box c.   Answer = 9

Question 5
Look carefully at the shapes.
Tick the shape that is not a triangle.   Answer =

Question 6
Find box d.
What is the difference between 18 and 13?
Write your answer in box d.   Answer = 5

Question 7
Find box e.
A fly has 6 legs.
How many legs do 3 flies have?
Write your answer in box e.   Answer = 18 legs

Name: _____

Question 1

0	1	2	3	4	5	6	7	8	9
10	11	12	13	14	15	16	17	18	19
20	21	22	23	24	25	26	27	28	29
30	31	32	33	34	35	36	37	38	39
40	41	42	43	44	45	46	47	48	49

Question 2

packets

a

Question 5

Question 3

ten(s)

b

Question 6

d

Question 4

c

Question 7

legs

e

Mental Arithmetic Test 19   Questions to be Read to the Children

Ask the children to look at their printed answer sheet.
Explain:
- *the boxes are for you to write your answers in;*
- *the letters below each box show you which box to use for each question;*
- *you can do any working out in the white spaces around the boxes, if you need to.*

Where necessary, you can show the children how to draw a tick, cross etc.
Remember to repeat each question.

Question 1
Look at the coins.
David wants to buy a new toy. The toy costs 45p.
Tick the coins he should use to give the correct amount.   Answer = 20p, 20p, 5p

---

Question 2
Find box a.
What is 3 less than 10?
Write your answer in box a.   Answer = 7

Question 3
Look at the graph above box b.
The graph shows different ways children travel to school.
How many more children walk to school than go in a car?
Write your answer in box b.   Answer = 6 children

Question 4
Look at the numbers in box c.
Circle the number that is nearest to ten.   Answer = ⑧

Question 5
Find box d.
What is 60 add 9?
Write your answer in box d.   Answer = 69

Question 6
Look at the drawing above box e.
What number is shown by the arrow?
Write your answer in box e.   Answer = 2

Question 7
Find box f.
What is the next number in this sequence?
10 – 20 – 30 – 40 – 50
Write your answer in box f.   Answer = 60

Question 8
Look at these 3D shapes.
Tick the sphere.   Answer =

Mental
Arithmetic
Test 19

Name: _____

Pupil Answer
Sheet

Question 1

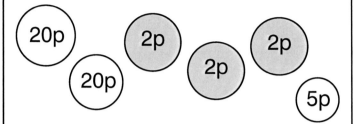

Question 5

d

Question 2

a

Question 6

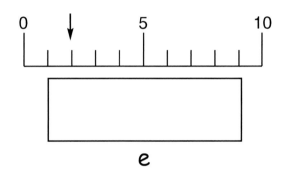

e

Question 3

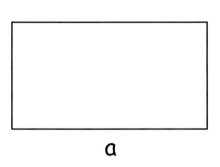

Ways children travel to school

children

b

Question 7

f

Question 4

8		5
	16	
15		20

c

Question 8

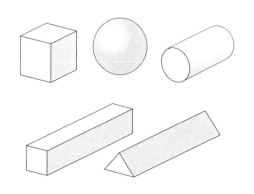

41

Mental Arithmetic Test 20   Questions to be Read to the Children

Ask the children to look at their printed answer sheet.
Explain:
* the boxes are for you to write your answers in;
* the letters below each box show you which box to use for each question;
* you can do any working out in the white spaces around the boxes, if you need to.

Where necessary, you can show the children how to draw a tick, cross etc.
Remember to repeat each question.

Question 1
Find box a.
There are 18 children in a class.
Half are boys and half are girls. How many children are girls?
Write your answer in box a.

Answer = 9 girls

Question 2
Find box b.
Think of one odd number that is more than 30 but less than 40.
Write your answer in box b.

(one of these:)
Answer = 31, 33, 35, 37, 39

Question 3
Find box c.
Listen to these numbers.
34 – 35 – 37 – 38
Write in box c the number I have missed out.

Answer = 36

Question 4
Find box d.
What is half of 14?
Write your answer in box d.

Answer = 7

Question 5
Look at the clock face.
Pat has her tea at 6 o'clock.
She goes to bed two and a half hours later.
Draw, on the clock face, the time she goes to bed.

Answer =

Question 6
Find box e.
Write one hundred and forty three as a number.
Write your answer in box e.

Answer = 143

Question 7
Find box f.
Robert has 10 candles on his birthday cake.
He blows out 9. How many candles are still lit?
Write your answer in box f.

Answer = 1 candle

Question 8
Look at these shapes.
Tick the shape that does not have a right angle.

Answer =

Mental
Arithmetic
Test 20

Name: _____

Pupil Answer
Sheet

Question 1

girls

a

Question 5

Question 2

b

Question 6

e

Question 3

c

Question 7

candle(s)

f

Question 4

d

Question 8

Mental Arithmetic Test 21   Questions to be Read to the Children

Ask the children to look at their printed answer sheet.
Explain:
- *the boxes are for you to write your answers in;*
- *the letters below each box show you which box to use for each question;*
- *you can do any working out in the white spaces around the boxes, if you need to.*

Where necessary, you can show the children how to draw a tick, cross etc.
Remember to repeat each question.

Question 1
Look at the graph above box a.
The graph shows favourite colours.
How many more children like blue than red?
Write your answer in box a.   Answer = 4 children

Question 2
Find box b.
What is 80 add 3?
Write your answer in box b.   Answer = 83

Question 3
Find box c.
One jug of water will fill 4 cups.
How many cups will 4 jugs of water fill?
Write your answer in box c .   Answer = 16 cups

Question 4
Look at the pieces of fruit.
Ross buys 2 pieces of fruit. They cost 50p altogether.
He paid 40p for a melon. Tick the other fruit he bought.   Answer = apple

---

Question 5
Find box d.
Anna is 5 years old. Her brother Owen is 4 years old.
How much older is Anna than Owen?
Write your answer in box d.   Answer = 1 year

Question 6
Look at the numbers in box e.
Circle the number that is the nearest 10 to 42.   Answer = (40)

Question 7
Find box f.
How many tens are there in 62?
Write your answer in box f.   Answer = 6 tens

Question 8
Look at the shapes.
Tick the shape that is not a hexagon.   Answer =

Mental
Arithmetic
Test 21

Name: _____

Pupil Answer
Sheet

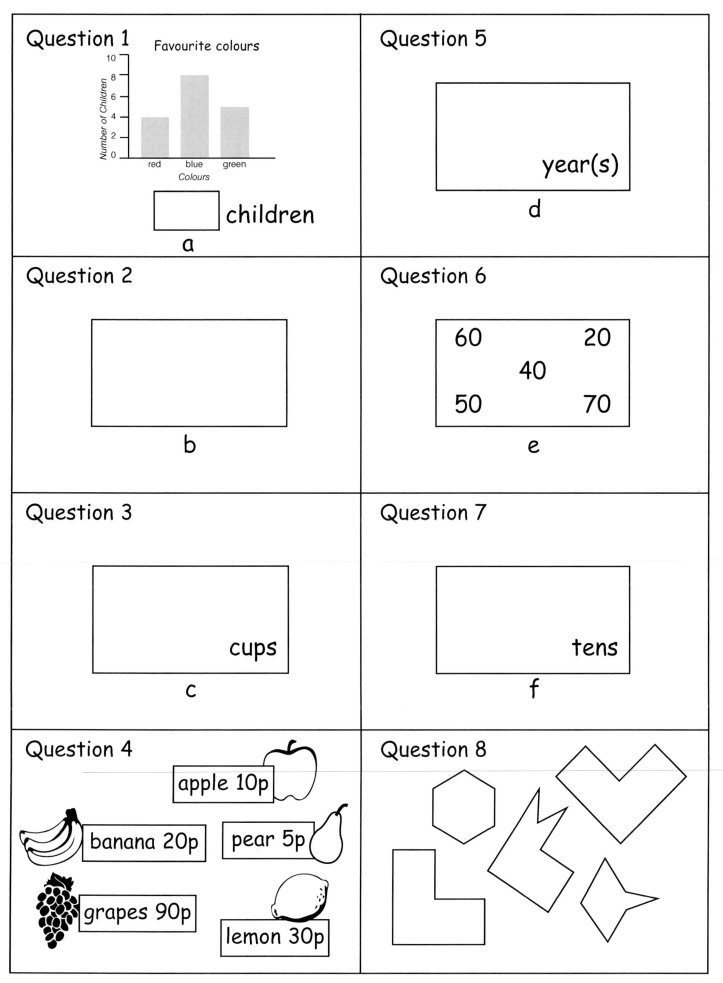

Question 1

Favourite colours

children
a

Question 2

b

Question 3

cups
c

Question 4

apple 10p
banana 20p
pear 5p
grapes 90p
lemon 30p

Question 5

year(s)
d

Question 6

60		20
	40	
50		70

e

Question 7

tens
f

Question 8

Ask the children to look at their printed answer sheet.
Explain:
* the boxes are for you to write your answers in;
* the letters below each box show you which box to use for each question;
* you can do any working out in the white spaces around the boxes, if you need to.

Where necessary, you can show the children how to draw a tick, cross etc.
Remember to repeat each question.

Question 1
Look at the grid.
I want you to find some numbers on the grid.
Put a ring around these numbers.
32 – 28 – 17

Answer = (32) (28) (17)

Question 2
Find box a.
What is the difference between 19 and 14?
Write your answer in box a.

Answer = 5

Question 3
Look at the clock face.
Amy gets home at 4 o'clock.
She goes to bed three and a half hours later.
Draw, on the clock face, the time she goes to bed.

Answer =

Question 4
Find box b.
What is 2 less than 15?
Write your answer in box b.

Answer = 13

Question 5
Look carefully at the shapes.
Tick the triangle.

Answer =

Question 6
Look at the numbers in box c.
Circle the number that is nearest to 20.

Answer = (19)

Question 7
Find box d.
What is the next number in this sequence?
2 – 4 – 6 – 8
Write your answer in box d.

Answer = 10

Name: _____

Question 1

0	1	2	3	4	5	6	7	8	9
10	11	12	13	14	15	16	17	18	19
20	21	22	23	24	25	26	27	28	29
30	31	32	33	34	35	36	37	38	39
40	41	42	43	44	45	46	47	48	49

Question 2

a

Question 5

Question 3

Question 6

19		42
	26	
10		17

c

Question 4

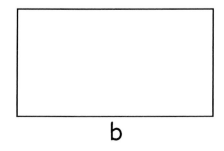

b

Question 7

d

Ask the children to look at their printed answer sheet.
Explain:
- *the boxes are for you to write your answers in;*
- *the letters below each box show you which box to use for each question;*
- *you can do any working out in the white spaces around the boxes, if you need to.*

Where necessary, you can show the children how to draw a tick, cross etc.
Remember to repeat each question.

Question 1
Find box a.
Jane had 4 balls. Amy had 5 balls.
How many balls did they have altogether?
Write your answer in box a.   Answer = 9 balls

Question 2
Find box b.
Write one hundred and five as a number.
Write your answer in box b.   Answer = 105

Question 3
Look at the drawing above box c.
What number is shown by the arrow?
Write your answer in box c.   Answer = 6

Question 4
Find box d.
Holly has 10 sweets. She eats 7 of them.
How many sweets does she have left?
Write your answer in box d.   Answer = 3 sweets

Question 5
Find box e.
What is 4 more than 13?
Write your answer in box e.   Answer = 17

Question 6
Find box f.
What is half of 8?
Write your answer in box f.   Answer = 4

Question 7
Find box g.
Think of one even number that is more than 30 but less than 40?   (On of these:)
Write your answer in box g.   Answer = 32, 34, 36, 38

Question 8
Look carefully at the shapes.
Tick the shape that does not have a right angle.   Answer =

Mental
Arithmetic
Test 23

Name: _____

Pupil Answer
Sheet

Question 1

balls

a

Question 2

b

Question 3

0   5   ↓   10

c

Question 4

sweets

d

Question 5

e

Question 6

f

Question 7

g

Question 8

Ask the children to look at their printed answer sheet.

Explain:

- *the boxes are for you to write your answers in;*
- *the letters below each box show you which box to use for each question;*
- *you can do any working out in the white spaces around the boxes, if you need to.*

Where necessary, you can show the children how to draw a tick, cross etc.
Remember to repeat each question.

Question 1
Look at the graph above box a.
This graph shows how children get to school.
How many more children travel by bus than car?
Write your answer in box a.   Answer = 2 children

Question 2
Find box b.
What is 70 add 4?
Write your answer in box b.   Answer = 74

Question 3
Find box c.
How many tens are in 47?
Write your answer in box c.   Answer = 4 tens

Question 4
Find box d.
There are 10 lollies in a box.
How many boxes do you need so 74 children can have 1 lolly each?
Write your answer in box d.   Answer = 8 boxes

Question 5
Find box e.
One spider has 8 legs. How many legs do 3 spiders have?
Write your answer in box e.   Answer = 24 legs

Question 6
Find box f.
Listen to these numbers.
46 – 47 – 49 – 50
Write the number I have missed in box f.   Answer = 48

Question 7
Look at the fruits.
Gill buys an apple for 15p and another fruit.
She spends 25p altogether.
Tick the second fruit she buys.   Answer = banana

Question 8
Look carefully at the shapes.
Put a cross on the shape that is not a hexagon.   Answer =

Name: _____

Question 1

Ways children travel to school

Number of Children

8
6
4
2
0

walk   bus   car

Transport

children

a

Question 2

b

Question 3

tens

c

Question 4

boxes

d

Question 5

legs

e

Question 6

f

Question 7

pear 15p

banana 10p

lemon 20p

kiwi 25p

Question 8

Mental Arithmetic Test 25   Questions to be Read to the Children

Ask the children to look at their printed answer sheet.
Explain:
- *the boxes are for you to write your answers in;*
- *the letters below each box show you which box to use for each question;*
- *you can do any working out in the white spaces around the boxes, if you need to.*

Where necessary, you can show the children how to draw a tick, cross etc.
Remember to repeat each question.

Question 1
Find box a.
Sarah is 5 years old. Amy is 2 years old.
How much older is Sarah than Amy?
Write your answer in box a.   Answer = 3 years

Question 2
Find box b.
What is 3 less than 11?
Write your answer in box b.   Answer = 8

Question 3
Look at the drawing above box c.
What number is shown by the arrow?
Write your answer in box c.   Answer = 4

Question 4
Find box d.
What is the difference between 16 and 12?
Write your answer in box d.   Answer = 4

Question 5
Look at the coins.
Jill wants to buy a pencil for 25p.
Tick the coins she should use to give the correct amount.   Answer = 10p, 10p, 5p

---

Question 6
Look at the numbers in box e.
Circle the number nearest to 37.   Answer = ④1

Question 7
Find box f.
There are 16 children in a group. Half are boys and half are girls.
How many children are boys?
Write your answer in box f.   Answer = 8 boys

Question 8
Listen carefully to the shape I am describing.
It has 5 sides. 4 sides are straight. 1 side is curved.
Tick the shape I have described.   Answer =

Name: _____

Question 1

years

a

Question 2

b

Question 3

0   ↓   5   10

c

Question 4

d

Question 5

10p 10p 10p 5p 2p 2p

Question 6

41		47
	32	
73		67

e

Question 7

boys

f

Question 8

Ask the children to look at their printed answer sheet.
Explain:
- *the boxes are for you to write your answers in;*
- *the letters below each box show you which box to use for each question;*
- *you can do any working out in the white spaces around the boxes, if you need to.*

Where necessary, you can show the children how to draw a tick, cross etc.
Remember to repeat each question.

Question 1
Look at the grid.
I want you to find some numbers on the grid.
Put a ring round these numbers. 38 – 26 - 47

Answer =   47

Question 2
Find box a.
Sam has 10 peas on his plate. 8 peas fall on the floor.
How many peas are left on the plate?
Write your answer in box a.

Answer = 2 peas

Question 3
Find box b.
Think of an odd number that is more than 20 but less than 60.
Write your answer in box b.

Answer = e.g. 33

Question 4
Find box c.
Write one hundred and twenty seven as a number.
Write your answer in box c.

Answer = 127

Question 5
Look carefully at the shapes.
Tick the pentagon.

Answer =

Question 6
Find box d.
Write the next number in this sequence.
3 – 6 – 9 – 12 – 15
Write your answer in box d.

Answer = 18

Question 7
Look at the numbers in box e.
Circle the number that is the nearest 10 to 69.

Answer =

Mental
Arithmetic
Test 26

Name: _____

Pupil Answer
Sheet

Question 1

0	1	2	3	4	5	6	7	8	9
10	11	12	13	14	15	16	17	18	19
20	21	22	23	24	25	26	27	28	29
30	31	32	33	34	35	36	37	38	39
40	41	42	43	44	45	46	47	48	49

Question 2

peas

a

Question 5

Question 3

b

Question 6

d

Question 4

c

Question 7

90   80

60

70   40

e

Ask the children to look at their printed answer sheet.
Explain:
- *the boxes are for you to write your answers in;*
- *the letters below each box show you which box to use for each question;*
- *you can do any working out in the white spaces around the boxes, if you need to.*

Where necessary, you can show the children how to draw a tick, cross etc.
Remember to repeat each question.

Question 1
Look at the cross in the circle.
If you move it through one half turn what position would it be in?
Tick one box for your answer.   Answer =

Question 2
Look at the graph above box a.
The graph shows children's favourite colours.
How many more children like red than green?
Write your answer in box a.   Answer = 5 children

Question 3
Find box b.
What is 2 more than 13?
Write your answer in box b.   Answer = 15

Question 4
Find box c.
What is half of 6?
Write your answer in box c.   Answer = 3

Question 5
Find box d.
How many tens are there in 68?
Write your answer in box d.   Answer = 6 tens

Question 6
Find box e.
What is 3 less than 9?
Write your answer in box e.   Answer = 6

Question 7
Find box f.
Barrow School starts at 9 o'clock.
Playtime is one and a half hours later.
What time does playtime start in Barrow School?   Answer = 10.30 or
Write your answer in box f.   half past ten

Question 8
Look carefully at the shapes.
Tick the shape with only 1 straight side.   Answer =

Question 3

6 more than 13

Question 4

half of 16.

5) as quest

6) 20 less than 60

7) as paper

8) as paper

Name____

subtract and colour.

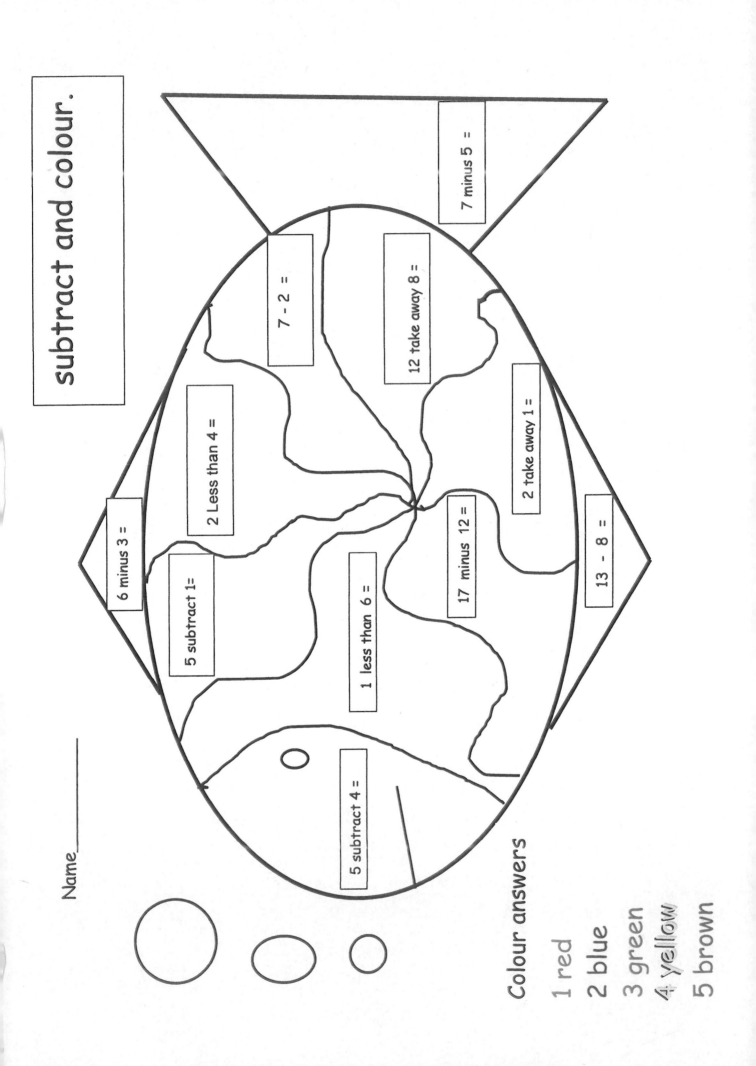

7 minus 5 =

7 - 2 =

2 Less than 4 =

12 take away 8 =

2 take away 1 =

6 minus 3 =

5 subtract 1=

1 less than 6 =

17 minus 12 =

13 - 8 =

5 subtract 4 =

Colour answers

1 red
2 blue
3 green
4 yellow
5 brown

Name: _____

Question 1

Question 5

tens

d

Question 2

Favourite Colours

Number of Children

10
8
6
4
2
0

blue   red   green

children

a

Question 6

e

Question 3

b

Question 7

f

Question 4

c

Question 8

57

Ask the children to look at their printed answer sheet.

Explain:

- *the boxes are for you to write your answers in;*
- *the letters below each box show you which box to use for each question;*
- *you can do any working out in the white spaces around the boxes, if you need to.*

Where necessary, you can show the children how to draw a tick, cross etc.
Remember to repeat each question.

Question 1
Find box a.
Listen to these numbers.
31 – 32 – 34 – 35
Write in box a the number I have missed out.

Answer = 33

Question 2
Find box b.
What is 60 add 8?
Write your answer in box b.

Answer = 68

Question 3
Find box c.
Helen has 6 apples. Fiona has 3 apples.
How many apples do they have altogether?
Write your answer in box c.

Answer = 9 apples

Question 4
Find box d.
There are 10 ice-creams in a box.
How many boxes do you need for 63 children to have one ice-cream each?
Write your answer in box d.

Answer = 7 boxes

Question 5
Look at the numbers in box e.
Circle the number that is the nearest 10 to 46.

Answer = (50)

Question 6
Look at the coins.
Eleanor wants to buy an orange for 12p.
Tick the coins she should use to give the correct amount.

Answer = 10p, 2p

Question 7
Look at the drawing above box f.
What number is shown by the arrow?
Write your answer in box f.

Answer = 3

Question 8
Look at the 3D shapes.
Tick the cylinder,

Answer =

Name: _____

Question 1

a

Question 5

| 50 | 40 |
| 60 | 30 |

e

Question 2

b

Question 6

10p   5p   2p   1p

Question 3

apples

c

Question 7

0   ↓   5   10

f

Question 4

boxes

d

Question 8

59

Ask the children to look at their printed answer sheet.
Explain:
• *the boxes are for you to write your answers in;*
• *the letters below each box show you which box to use for each question;*
• *you can do any working out in the white spaces around the boxes, if you need to.*

Where necessary, you can show the children how to draw a tick, cross etc.
Remember to repeat each question.

Question 1
Find box a.
Olivia is 4 years old. Jane is 7 years old.
How much older is Jane than Olivia?
Write your answer in box a.   Answer = 3 years

Question 2
Find box b.
There are 14 children in a group.
Half of the children are boys.
How many girls are in the group?
Write your answer in box b.   Answer = 7 girls

Question 3
Find box c.
What is the difference between 17 and 13?
Write your answer in box c.   Answer = 4

Question 4
Look at the clock face.
Jenny's school starts at 9 o'clock.
Jenny was half an hour late for school.
Draw, on the clock face, the time Jenny arrived at school.   Answer =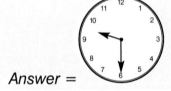

Question 5
Find box d.
Mrs Gillet has 3 boxes. Each box has 4 pencils inside.
How many pencils does Mrs Gillet have altogether?
Write your answer in box d.   Answer = 12

Question 6
Look at the numbers in box e.
Circle the number nearest to 48.   Answer = (50)

Question 7
Look at the fruit.
Joshua spent 20p.
He bought an apple for 8p and another fruit.
Tick the other fruit he bought.   Answer = lemon

Question 8
Look at the shapes.
Put a cross on the shape that has no right angle.   Answer =

Mental
Arithmetic
Test 29

Name: _____

Pupil Answer
Sheet

Question 1

years

a

Question 2

girls

b

Question 3

c

Question 4

Question 5

pencils

d

Question 6

42		64
	18	
50		86

e

Question 7

pear 9p

banana 15p

orange 10p

lemon 12p

Question 8

61

Ask the children to look at their printed answer sheet.
Explain:
- *the boxes are for you to write your answers in;*
- *the letters below each box show you which box to use for each question;*
- *you can do any working out in the white spaces around the boxes, if you need to.*

Where necessary, you can show the children how to draw a tick, cross etc.
Remember to repeat each question.

Question 1
Look at the grid.
I want you to find some numbers on the grid.
Put a ring around these numbers.
44 – 37 – 26

Answer = 44 37 26

Question 2
Find box a.
Think of one even number which is more than 30 and less than 50.
Write your answer in box a.

Answer = e.g. 42

Question 3
Find box b.
What is the next number in this sequence?
5 – 10 – 15 – 20
Write your answer in box b.

Answer = 25

Question 4
Find box c.
Daniel is thinking of a number. The number is 6 more than 10.
What number is Daniel thinking of?
Write your answer in box c.

Answer = 16

Question 5
Look carefully at the shapes.
Put a cross in the shape that is not a pentagon.

Answer =

Question 6
Find box d.
Bethany has 10 candles on her cake. She blows out 6 candles.
How many candles are left burning?
Write your answer in box d.

Answer = 4 candles

Question 7
Find box e.
Write one hundred and six as a number.
Write your answer in box e.

Answer = 106

Name: _____

Question 1

0	1	2	3	4	5	6	7	8	9
10	11	12	13	14	15	16	17	18	19
20	21	22	23	24	25	26	27	28	29
30	31	32	33	34	35	36	37	38	39
40	41	42	43	44	45	46	47	48	49

Question 2

a

Question 3

b

Question 4

c

Question 5

Question 6

candles

d

Question 7

e

Teacher's Record Sheet

Class _____   Date Started _____

N.B. All tests are marked out of 8 except for those shaded, which are marked out of 7.

Pupil's Name	Test 1	Test 2	Test 3	Test 4	Test 5	Test 6	Test 7	Test 8	Test 9	Test 10	Test 11	Test 12	Test 13	Test 14	Test 15	Test 16	Test 17	Test 18	Test 19	Test 20	Test 21	Test 22	Test 23	Test 24	Test 25	Test 26	Test 27	Test 28	Test 29	Test 30